Preschool MathSmart
Activities

ISBN: 978-1-77149-065-8

Printed in China

CONTENTS

1

Tracing Fun

Trace.

A. Trace.

B. Trace.

C. Trace.

D. Trace.

E. Trace.

F. Trace.

G. Trace.

H. Trace.

I. Cut out the pictures on page 15 and paste them in the correct spaces. Then trace.

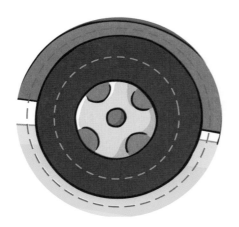
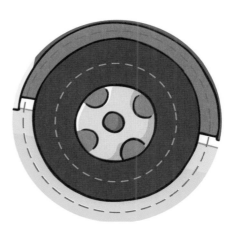

2 Sort Things Out

Trace to show where the apple belongs.

A. Trace. Then cross out the one that has a different colour.

B.   Trace. Then cross out the one that has a different pattern.

C. Trace. Then draw lines to put the foods in the correct groups.

D. Trace. Then draw lines to put the things in the correct groups.

E. Cut out the objects on page 23 and paste them in the correct boxes.

F. Cut out the correct objects and paste them in the box.

Toys

G. Put the animal stickers in the correct places.

H. Draw lines to lead the vehicles to where they belong.

Match Things Up

Colour each pair of shoes the same colour.

A. Put the wheel stickers in the correct circles.

B. **Help the children find their matching pairs. Put the stickers in the correct boxes.**

C. Help Sally match the outfits. Cut out the matching outfits on page 33 and paste them in the boxes.

D. Colour each matching pair with the same colour. Cross out the one without a match.

E. Trace the lines to give the children the correct tools.

F.   Cut out the correct tools and paste them in the boxes.

G. **Find Mommy Pig's baby. Cut out the correct picture and paste it in the box.**

From Small to Big

big  small

Trace the small ones.

A. Colour the big ones for Daddy Bear.

B. Colour the balloons of the same size with the same colour.

C. The bears have put on some things that do not fit them. Circle those things.

D. Colour the bees and the flowers with the correct colours.

small

smaller

big

bigger

E. Put your hand over the bear's pawprint. Trace your hand and circle the correct word to describe your hand.

I think mine is bigger.

My hand is **bigger** / **smaller** .

F. **Cut out the mice and paste them in the correct boxes.**

smallest

smaller

small

G. Find the balloon stickers on the sticker sheet. Give each bear a balloon according to its size.

H. Circle the smallest vehicle and the biggest house.

smallest   **biggest**

I.   Cut out the animals and paste them in the correct boxes.

smallest ➡ *biggest*

5 Which Is Taller?

tall   short

Colour the tall pile.

A. Cut out the taller building on page 55 and paste it beside the tower.

B. **Colour the shorter tree.**

C. Draw the trees.

tall   taller   tallest

D.   Cut out the flowers and paste them in the correct boxes.

short   shorter   shortest

E. Put the animal stickers in order from tallest to shortest. Then circle the correct animal.

tallest  **shortest**

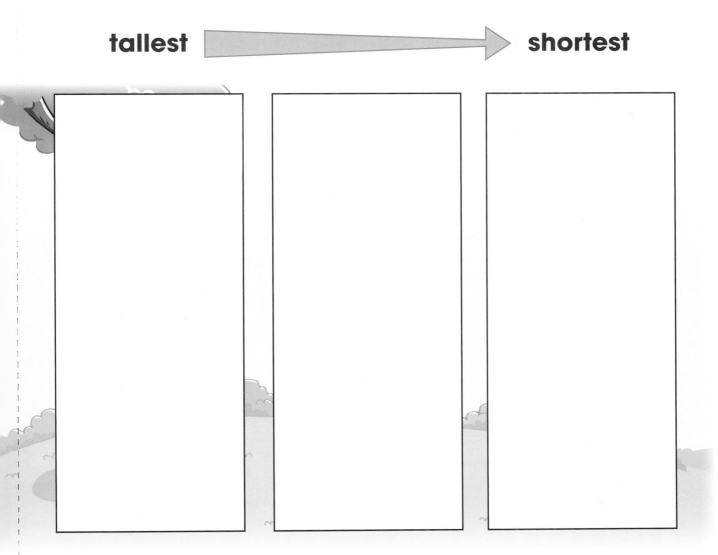

Who is shorter than I?

F.   Cut out the correct faces on page 63 and paste them in the circles.

shortest: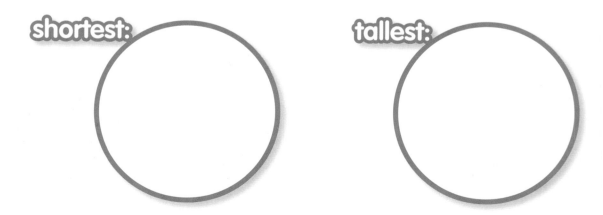

tallest:

6 Long or Short?

short

long

Colour the long legs green and the short legs red.

A. Sally and Tim got haircuts today. Cut out the correct pictures on page 67 and paste them in the boxes.

Sally

long hair

short hair

Thank you, Mrs. Green.

Tim

long hair

short hair

Sally

Tim

B. Draw lines to match the animals with their tails. Then circle the correct animal.

Let's find our tails.

The 🐷 / 🐹 has a shorter tail.

C. Read Peter's question. Trace and colour the correct train.

Which train is **longer**?

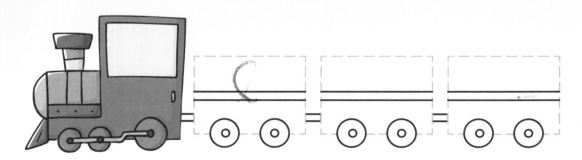

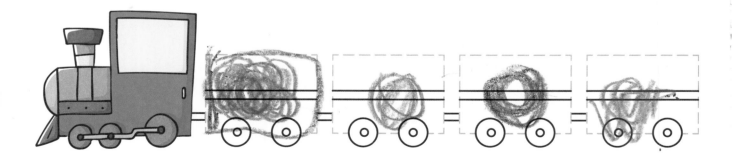

D. Cut out the pairs of shorts and paste them in the correct boxes.

short   shorter   shortest

E. Trace the fishing lines. Then put the fish stickers in the correct boxes.

Fishing line

long:

longer:

longest:

F. Trace the spider silk. Circle the spider that makes the longest silk.

G. Colour the bars on the xylophone.

shortest

longest

H. Trace. Then put the worm stickers in order.

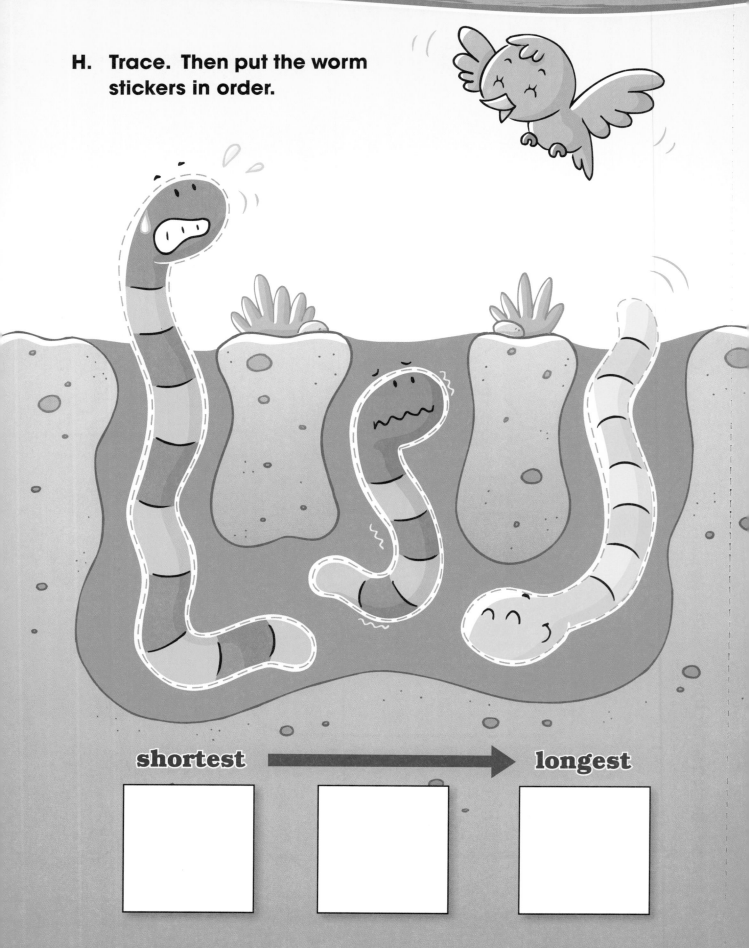

shortest ➡ longest

7 How Wide? How Thick?

thin   thick

Draw lines to put the thin slices of bread into the toaster.

A. **Draw a line through the wide tunnel to lead the snail to the water.**

B. Put the door stickers on the houses. Then lead the boy to the house with the narrow door.

C. Look at the wings of the butterflies on the sticker sheet. Put the stickers in the correct circles.

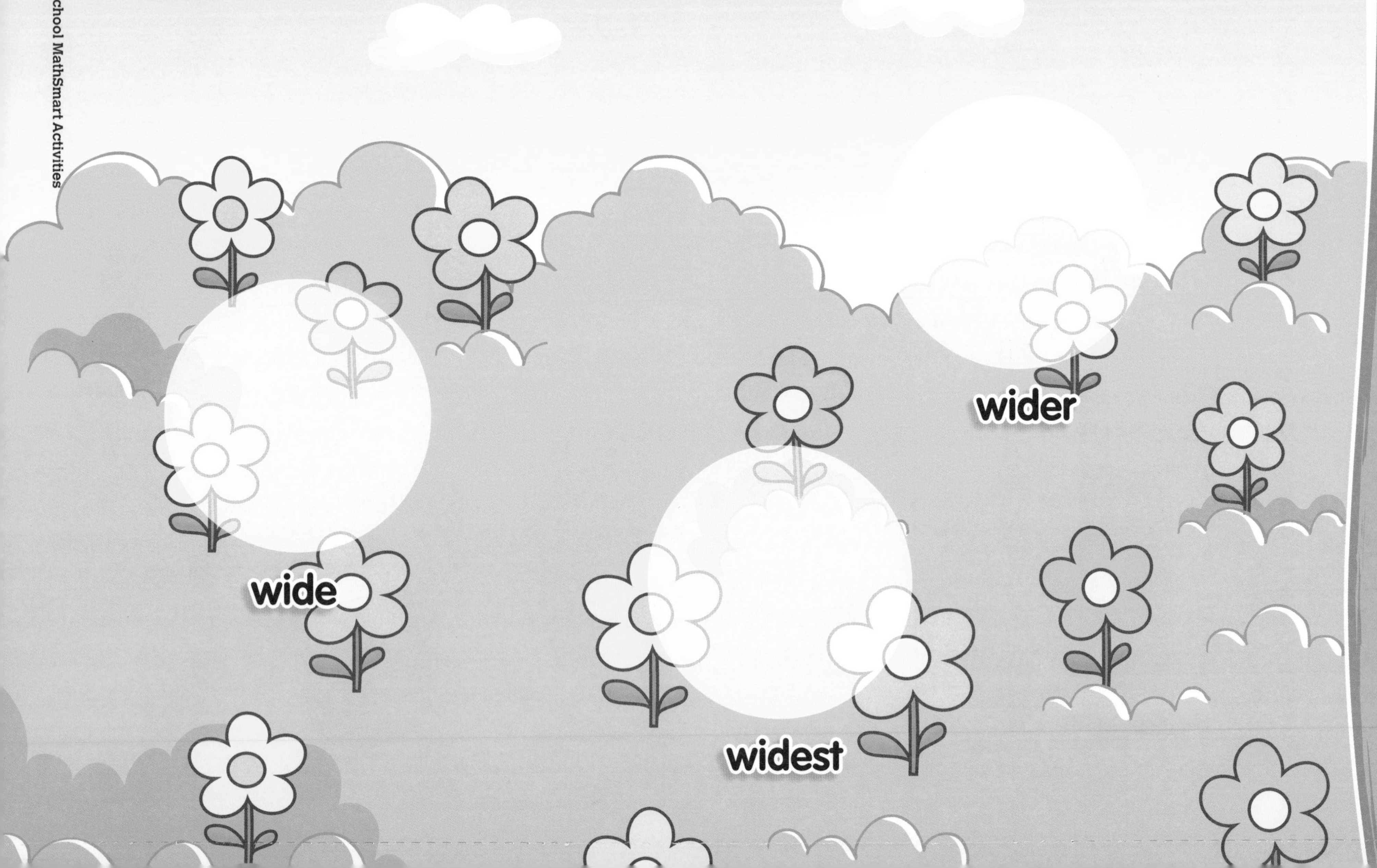

wider

widest

wide

D. Put the sticker of Goldilocks on the widest bed. Then put the window sticker above the narrowest bed.

E. Colour the thick chopping board. Then colour the food in thick slices.

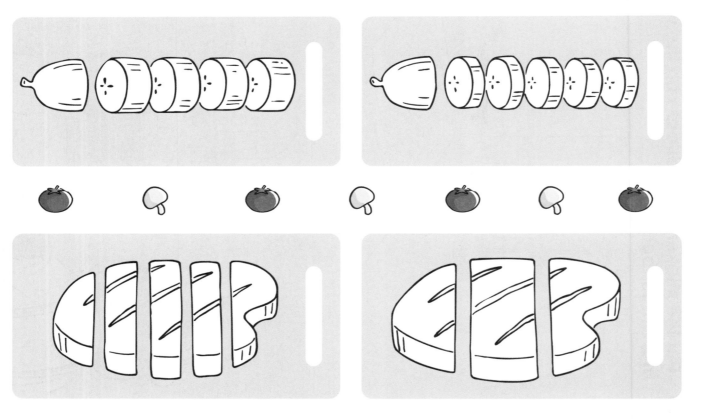

F. Colour the correct blocks of cheese with the given colours.

thinnest

thickest

G. Cut out the thicker ingredients on page 85 and paste them below to help Chef Tim make a thick hamburger.

H. Cut out the stools and paste them in the correct boxes.

wide

wider

widest

8

Is It Heavy?

light

heavy

Colour the heavy object green and the light object yellow.

A. Put the stickers of heavy objects in the boxes.

Heavy

B.   Put the stickers of light objects in the boxes.

C. Colour the heavy objects.

D. Cut out the light objects and paste them in the boxes.

E. Circle the lighter object in each pair. Then trace the lines to give them to Mr. Smith.

Thank you!

F. Cut out the objects on page 97 and paste them in order from lightest to heaviest.

G. Find the three pairs of differences. Colour the heavier object in each pair.

H. Each child is holding the heaviest object in each group. Draw the objects in their hands.

the heaviest

9

More and More

Colour the group with more acorns.

more

fewer

A. Cut out the correct number of meals on page 103 and paste them on the table to serve the children.

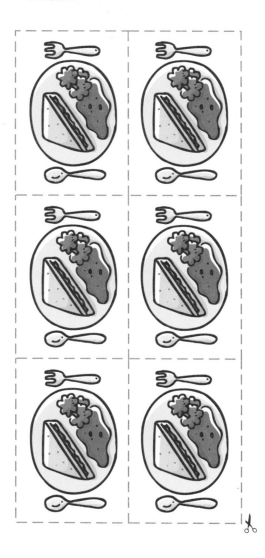

B.   Give each child a balloon sticker.

C. Colour to add more water into the fish tank. Then draw more fish.

Lucy's Lollipops

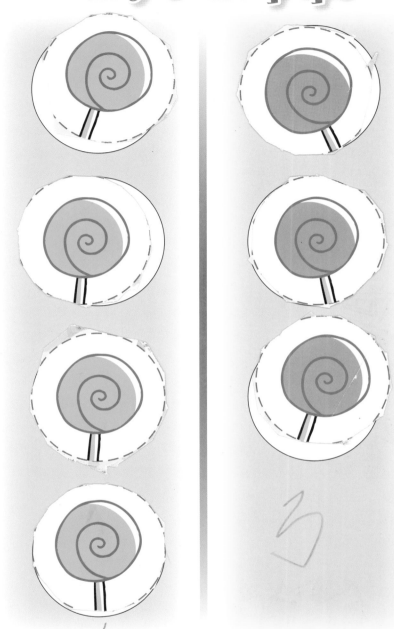

Colour the lollipop that Lucy has more.

Lucy has more  .

E. Put the animal stickers in the correct groups. Then put the word stickers in the correct speech boxes.

F. Circle the teeth that have been knocked down. Then colour the winner who knocked down more teeth.

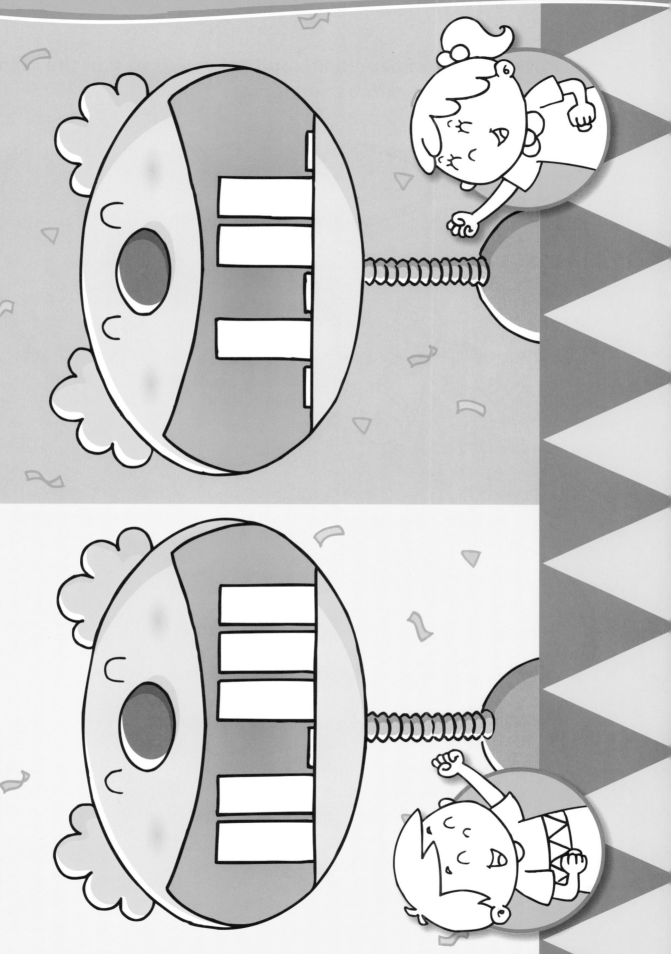

G. Put the horse sticker in the correct group so that the children have the same number of horses.

10

Numbers 1 to 10

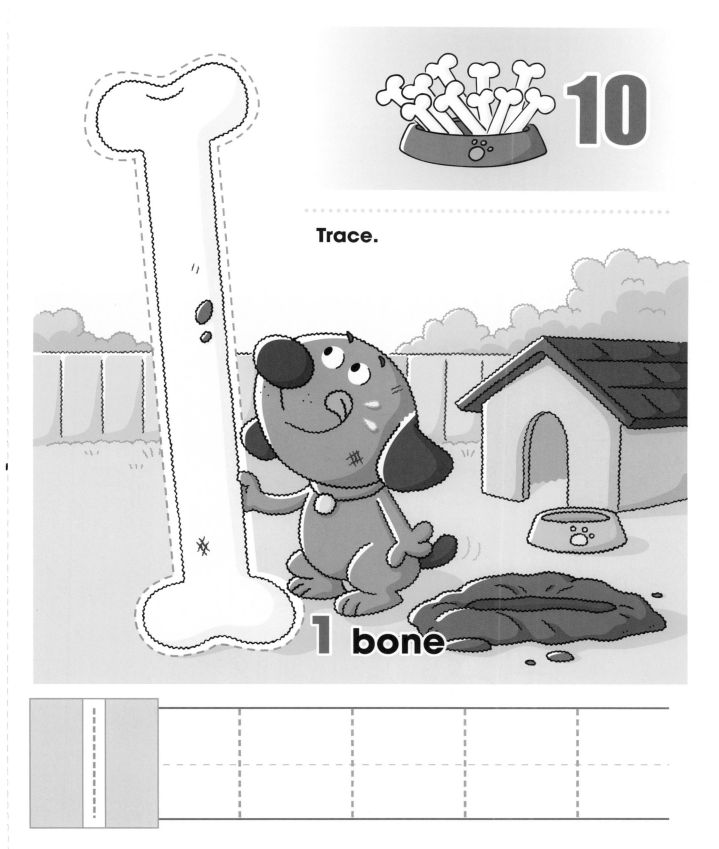

10

Trace.

1 bone

A. Trace. Then circle the 2 butterflies.

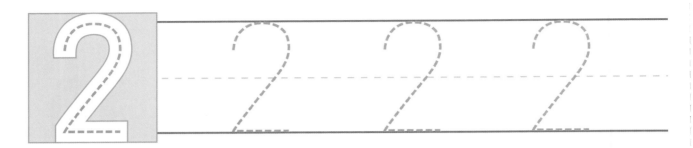

2 butterflies

B. Trace. Then colour the 3 pigs.

3 pigs

C. Trace. Then put the 4 ball stickers in the circles.

4 balls

D. Trace. Then colour the 5 fish.

5 fish

E. **Trace. Then draw a line to lead the bus to take the 6 children to school.**

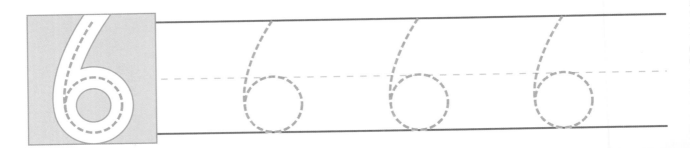

6 children

F. **Trace. Then put the flower stickers in the circles.**

7 **flowers**

G. Trace the number. Then trace the line to help the puppy take the 8 bones to his house.

8 bones

H. Trace. Then colour the 9 carrots.

9 carrots

I.   Trace the number and the 10 bubbles.

10 bubbles

J. Find and circle all the numbers.

K. Colour to see the hidden object.

Unit 1

Tracing Fun

p. 5 (Trace.)
A – H. (Trace.)
I.

Unit 2

Sort Things Out

p. 17 (Trace.)
A. (Trace.)

B. (Trace.)

C. (Trace.)

D. (Trace.)

E.

F.

G.

H.

Unit 3

Match Things Up

p. 29

A.

B.

C.

D.

E.

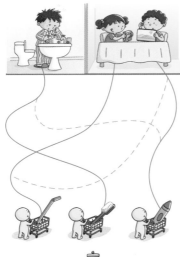

F.

G.

Unit 4

From Small to Big

p. 41

A.

B.

C.

D.

E. (Individual answers)

F.

G.

H. smallest: biggest:

I.

Unit 5
Which Is Taller?

p. 53

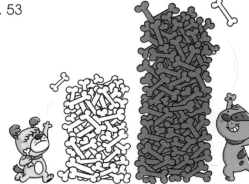

A.

B.

C.

D.

E.

F.

Unit 6
Long or Short?
p. 65

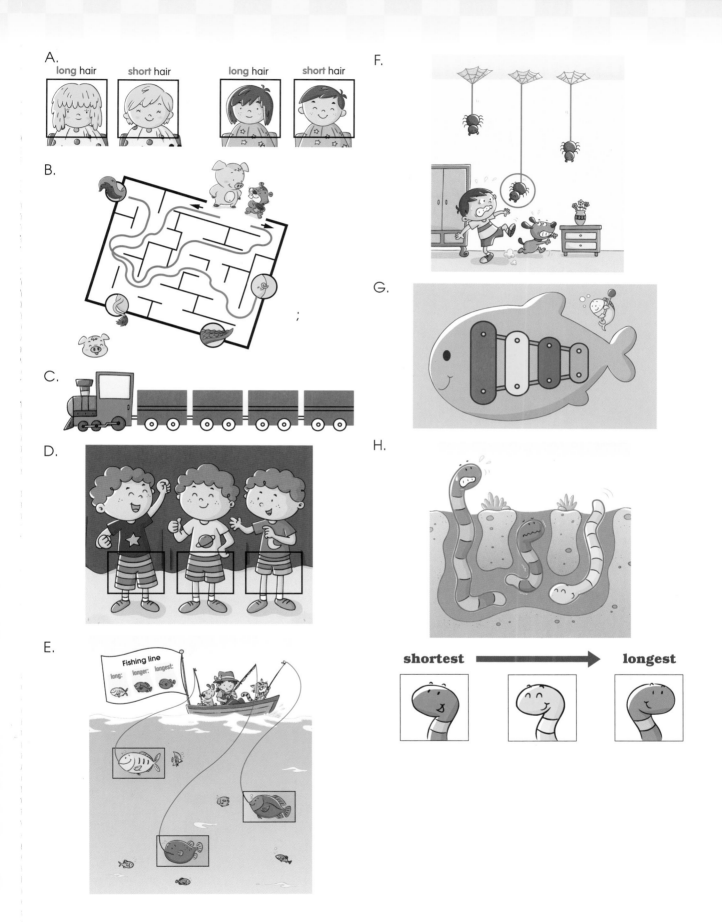

A.

long hair   short hair   long hair   short hair

B.

C.

D.

E.

Fishing line

long: longer: longest:

F.

G.

H.

shortest ➞ **longest**

Unit 7

How Wide? How Thick?

p. 77

A.

B.

C.

D.

E.

F.

G.

H.

Unit 8

Is It Heavy?

p. 89

A.

B.

C.

D.

Light

E.

F.

A.

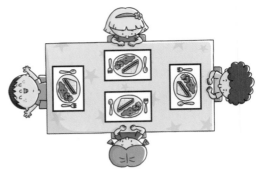

G.

B.

H.

C.

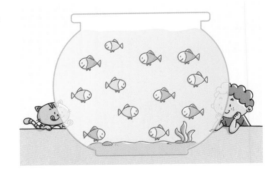

Unit 9
More and More

p. 101

D.

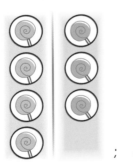

E.

Unit 10

Numbers 1 to 10

p. 113 (Trace.)
A. (Trace.)

F.

B. (Trace and colour.)
C. (Trace.)

G.

D. (Trace and colour.)
E. (Trace.)

F. (Trace.)

G. (Trace.)

H. (Trace and colour.)
I. (Trace.)
J.

K.

How to Play the Game:
Circus Fun

- two game pieces
  (e.g. erasers, bottle caps, coins)
- a dice

1 Place your game pieces here.

2 You can go first.

Roll the dice and move your game piece.

3

Math Card

If you land on, pick a **Math Card** from the deck.

Take turns until...

4 You win!

✔ : Move 2 steps forward.
✗ : Move 1 step backward.

Math Card

✔ : Move 2 steps forward.
✗ : Move 1 step backward.

Math Card

✔ : Move 2 steps forward.
✗ : Move 1 step backward.

Math Card

✔ : Move 2 steps forward.
✗ : Move 1 step backward.

Math Card

✔ : Move 2 steps forward.
✗ : Move 1 step backward.

Math Card

✔ : Move 2 steps forward.
✗ : Move 1 step backward.

Math Card

Who has shorter ears?

The longest path leads Sue to the...

Which sock matches mine?

Which cake is thicker?

Point to the coin that does not belong.

Point to the longer rope.

✔ : Move 2 steps forward.	✔ : Move 2 steps forward.
✗ : Move 1 step backward.	✗ : Move 1 step backward.

Math Card

Math Card

✔ : Move 2 steps forward.	✔ : Move 2 steps forward.
✗ : Move 1 step backward.	✗ : Move 1 step backward.

Math Card

Math Card

✔ : Move 2 steps forward.	✔ : Move 2 steps forward.
✗ : Move 1 step backward.	✗ : Move 1 step backward.

Math Card

Math Card

✔ : Move 2 steps forward.
✗ : Move 1 step backward.

Math Card

✔ : Move 2 steps forward.
✗ : Move 1 step backward.

Math Card

✔ : Move 2 steps forward.
✗ : Move 1 step backward.

Math Card

✔ : Move 2 steps forward.
✗ : Move 1 step backward.

Math Card

✔ : Move 2 steps forward.
✗ : Move 1 step backward.

Math Card

✔ : Move 2 steps forward.
✗ : Move 1 step backward.

Math Card

Math Card

✔ : Move 2 steps forward.
✗ : Move 1 step backward.

Math Card

✔ : Move 2 steps forward.
✗ : Move 1 step backward.

Math Card

✔ : Move 2 steps forward.
✗ : Move 1 step backward.

Math Card

✔ : Move 2 steps forward.
✗ : Move 1 step backward.

Math Card

✔ : Move 2 steps forward.
✗ : Move 1 step backward.

Math Card

✔ : Move 2 steps forward.
✗ : Move 1 step backward.

Math Card